BucQUEENham Palace

DAVID GAMBLE

Cover illustration by Roger FitzGerald

WEALD ARTOIS
Publications

BUCKINGHAM PALACE FROM THE PARK
CIRCA 1840

BucQUEENham Palace

"It's very strange," said the girl, "that BucKINGham Palace has a KING in it."

"No, it's not," scoffed the boy, "that's not strange at all, because that's where the KING lives and the word fits neatly inside BucKINGham."

"Well, when was the last time a king lived in Buckingham Palace?" asked the girl sharply.

"Er, about 1965, I guess," dithered the boy who really had no idea.

"Miles out," laughed the girl.

"What is the answer then?" replied the boy, a bit miffed at being laughed at.

"To be accurate, it was February 6th, 1952 when King George VI died. That's the day before Grandad's seventh birthday," advised the girl who had the facts at her fingertips, because she had been googling them and asking Grandad too for extra information.

"Oh," said the boy, "but there were several kings before him. Like two Edwards and another George."

"Yes, you are right. Edward VII, George V and then, for a very short time, Edward VIII," trotted out the girl.

"There," said the boy, "I told you it is where kings live. Look at the stamps that Grandad sent us. Four kings!"

"True," pondered the girl, "but Edward VII became king when his mother, Queen Victoria died in January 1901."

"So," said the boy, who was good at mental arithmetic, "that means that there have been kings in BucKINGham Palace for 51 years from 1901 to 1952."

"Oh yes," smiled the girl mischievously, "you're absolutely right. Do you think that's why BucKINGham Palace has a king in its name?"

"Of course," said the boy, "it's obvious."

"Really?" asked the girl. "Well, how long did Victoria live in BucKINGham Palace?"

"Let me see. She was crowned in..." the boy paused.

"1837 when she was 18," supplied the girl.

"That means she was Queen and living in BucKINGham Palace for over 63 years," calculated the boy.

"Well done, "exclaimed the girl, "she was the first queen or king to live in BucKINGham Palace. She lived there longer than all the four kings put together! Look, here are her stamps and some of them show her as a young girl and then later as an old lady."

"I suppose you're right," sulked the boy who could see where all this calculating was going.

"Not only am I right about Queen Victoria," squeaked the girl in her excitement, "but do you know how long Queen Elizabeth II has been Queen?"

The boy thought carefully, "Well, from 1952 to now."

"And how long is that?" asked the girl.

"Now then," said the boy, "2021 minus 1952 is 69 years and counting."

"So, if we put Queen Victoria's reign and our Queen's reign together we get 132 years. That's far more than all those kings." The girl was delighted.

"In fact, 81 years more," she went on, while looking at the stamps of Queen Elizabeth from Grandad's collection.

"These are very jolly stamps of Queen Elizabeth," she laughed, "she seems to be having a good time."

"Grandad says the Queen probably had a hand in choosing them. He says she always approves the designs of British stamps." said the boy.

"Returning to the 81 years more for queens in the Palace," the girl continued, "even if Princes Charles and William and then George become King, it will take them a long time to catch up with the queens. George was born in 2013, so he is eight now and in 79 years, in 2100, he will be 87. So, at the turn of the century the kings are almost drawing level with the queens. I hope our Queen will keep going for more years and if so, then George could be well into his nineties before BucKINGham Palace deserves its name."

"OK, clever clogs," retorted the boy, "what are you going to do about it?"

"I shall write to the Queen and ask her to change the name of her palace to BucQUEENham Palace. That will set the record straight," said the girl determinedly.

"But after George is King and somewhere in his nineties then they will have to change the name back to BucKINGham Palace again," pointed out the boy.

"I don't know," mused the girl, "imagine if George's first child is a daughter, then we will be back to queens again and they clearly stick around a long time. No, I think BucQUEENham Palace may be here to stay."

"Well, I don't understand that stuff about the first child," retorted the boy. "Who comes next is all too complicated."

"Let's ask Grandad, he may know," said the girl gently and they went off to zoom him.

Grandad listened to their stories, chuckled at some of their ideas and suggested that they zoom again in a week, by which time he would have something to show them.

A week later on zoom Grandad started by saying, "It's quite right that if George's first child is a girl, then we would have a queen again. Parliament changed the law in 2013 so that boys and girls are treated equally for the succession after that date. The elder will become the sovereign."

"About time too," said the girl.

"I've also made a simple direct line of succession for you from Victoria down to young George," Grandad went on.

"Oh," said the boy, "I can follow that."

Queen Victoria — Prince Albert, Prince Consort

King Edward VII — Alexandra, Queen

King George V — Mary, Queen

King Edward VIII — Wallis, Duchess of Windsor

King George VI — Elizabeth, Queen (The Queen Mother)

Queen Elizabeth II — Prince Philip, Duke of Edinburgh

Prince Charles — Princess Diana
Camilla, Duchess of Cornwall

Prince William — Catherine, Duchess of Cambridge

Prince George

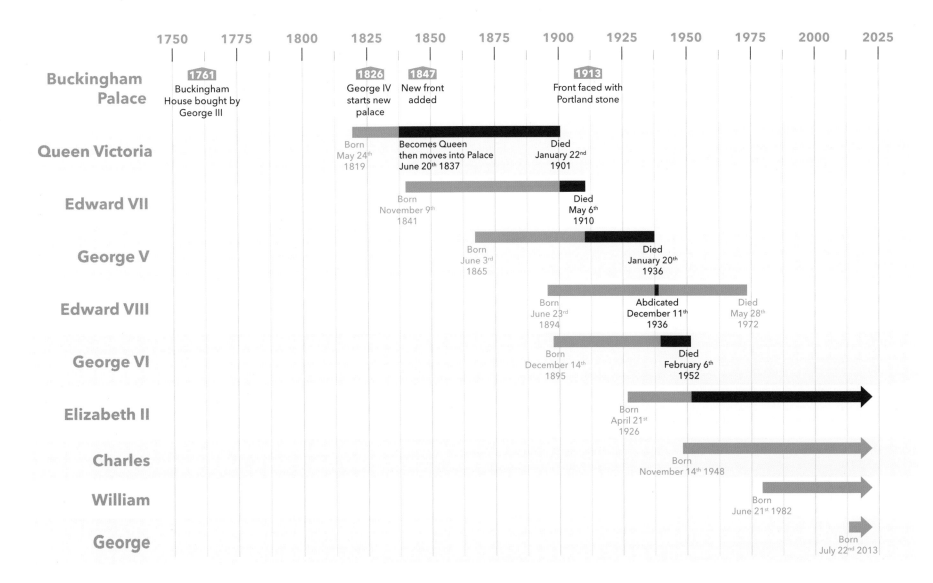

"So that you can better understand how long the Kings and Queens were living in the Palace I have created this diagram, which hopefully makes it clearer," said Grandad. "The darker lines show their reigns."

"It certainly does," cried the girl. "The Queens have definitely been at the Palace much longer than the Kings."

The boy said nothing.

"And I've dug out some photographs that show the Royal Family together," said Grandad holding them up.

The boy and girl leaned forward to get a better look.

"What about these groups?" asked the boy.

"The first one is from an old magazine. You can see Victoria with Edward, her son, later King Edward VII, and on the left, George, her grandson, later King George V, with Edward, her great-grandson in the sailor suit. He became King Edward VIII."

"They look very solemn," said the girl.

"In those days they had to stand very still or the photo would come out blurred," explained Grandad.

"What's the cushion for?" asked the boy.

"I'm not sure, maybe it's to keep her feet warm."

The Queen, Prince of Wales, Duke of York and Prince Edward of York.

"There is this one after the coronation of King George VI in 1937. They are on the balcony of the Palace," he continued.

"How lovely," cried the girl. "They've got their crowns on!"

"Yes, Queen Elizabeth, known to us as the Queen Mother, and the King look very splendid," said Grandad.

"So, who are the two little girls?" asked the boy. "They look like they are enjoying themselves."

"On the left is Princess Elizabeth, now our Queen, and the other is Princess Margaret, her sister," said Grandad. "The older lady is King George's mother, Queen Mary. She is a very strong link between Queen Victoria and our present Queen, because she was born in 1867 and would have known Victoria fairly well. She spent a lot of time with her granddaughter Elizabeth and she died in 1953, a few months before Elizabeth's coronation."

"In this one, the Royal Family is again on the balcony, after the Trooping of the Colour, watching the flypast. Can you work out who is who?" he asked.

"Well," said the girl excitedly, "there's Prince Charles, Catherine carrying Charlotte, Prince George, Prince William with Harry

behind him, then the Queen, Prince Philip and Sophie, Prince Edward's wife, with her son James."

"Is George saluting?" asked the boy.

"He might be," replied Grandad, " but I rather think he's shading his eyes to see the flypast better."

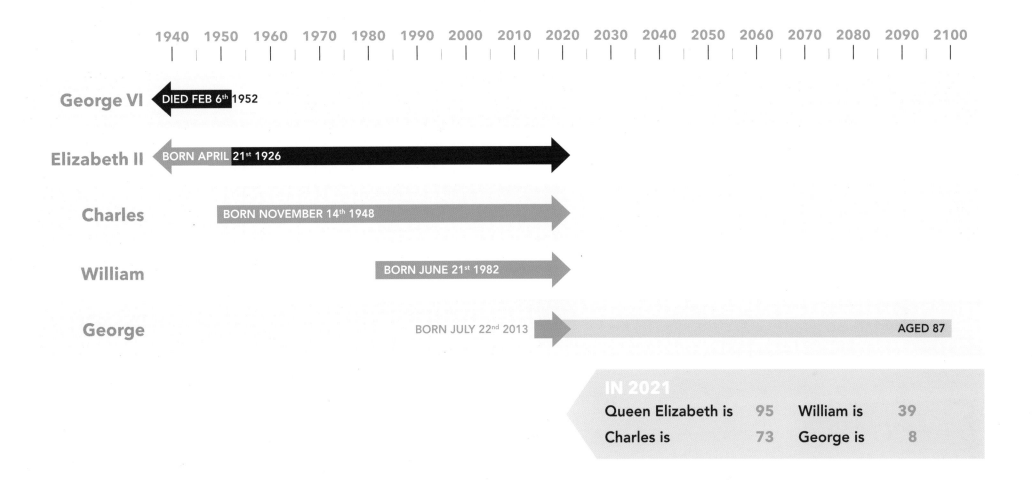

1940 1950 1960 1970 1980 1990 2000 2010 2020 2030 2040 2050 2060 2070 2080 2090 2100

George VI ← DIED FEB 6th 1952

Elizabeth II ← BORN APRIL 21st 1926 →

Charles BORN NOVEMBER 14th 1948 →

William BORN JUNE 21st 1982 →

George BORN JULY 22nd 2013 → AGED 87

IN 2021

Queen Elizabeth is	95	William is	39
Charles is	73	George is	8

"Now have a look at this," said Grandad. "I created another chart on my computer to show how old each member of the Royal Family in the direct line of succession is today. You see in 2021 Prince George is eight, but in 2100, which seems a long time off, how old will he be?"

"He'll be 87!" cried the boy. "Why, that's even older than you, Grandad!"

Grandad laughed. "That's enough of that."

"What else have you found?" the girl asked.

"I've unearthed a lot about the Palace and how it has been changed. Would you like to see the pictures?"

"Yes, please," they said in unison.

"Look, here is the original Buckingham House which was built in 1703 for the Duke of Buckingham. That's where the name comes from. At that time it was surrounded by woods and fields. King George III bought it in 1761 and gave it to his young wife, Queen Charlotte.

They carried on using St. James' Palace as their official residence, but they must have liked Buckingham House because Queen Charlotte had 14 of her 15 children there."

"15 kids!" shrieked the girl. "No wonder they needed a palace."

"Remember it wasn't a palace when she lived there," said Grandad. "She was only 17 when she married. You know three of her children became kings and Victoria was her granddaughter."

"Why did it change from a house to a palace?" asked the girl.

"Ah," said Grandad," it seems that George IV, who loved building amazing palaces, was not satisfied with Buckingham House and he got his architect, John Nash, to start building something grander. George IV ran out of money and after he died, his brother William IV did not want the Palace, which still needed further work."

"This is what Buckingham Palace first looked like," he went on. "This is the view from St. James' Park. It was built around a large courtyard with two wings and, at the front, they placed the Marble Arch."

"I thought that was somewhere at the end of Oxford Street," said the boy.

"In fact, it was in a corner of Hyde Park called Cumberland Gate. It was moved there in 1851, partly because they wanted the Marble Arch as an entrance for people visiting the Great Exhibition in Hyde Park."

"Did it take long to move?" asked the boy.

"It was all done in three months," said Grandad.

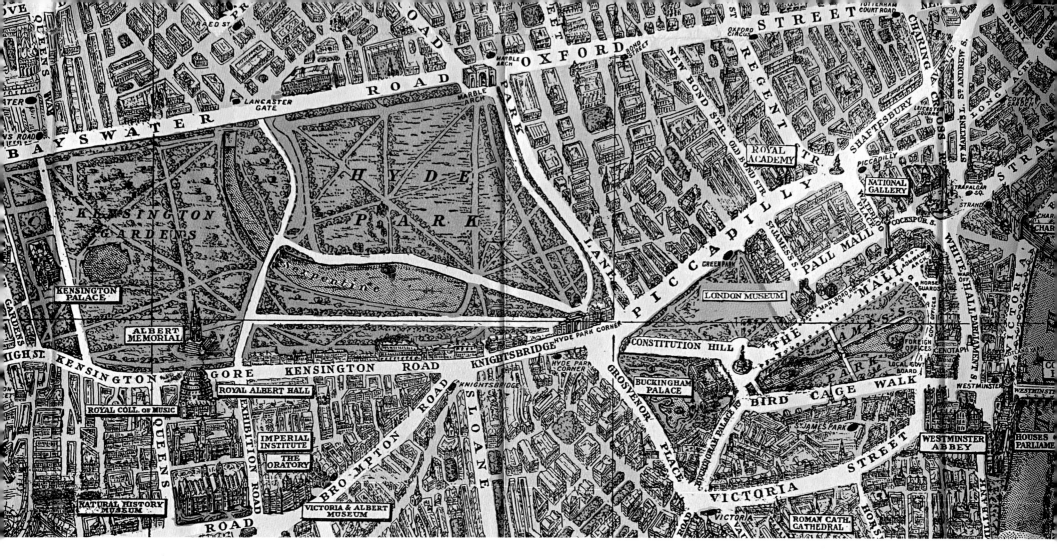

"Can we walk through it now to go to Hyde Park?" asked the girl.

"No, sadly the new road system has cut it off from the park," replied Grandad, putting up an old map of the area on screen. "Have a look and see if you can find the Palace and the Marble Arch."

"The Palace is at the end of the Mall," cried the girl, "but I can't find Marble Arch."

"There it is," crowed the boy. "In the top right corner of Hyde Park."

"What was the point of Marble Arch anyway?" asked the boy.

"It was built to celebrate the victories of Nelson and Wellington at Trafalgar and Waterloo. Of course, when it came to celebrating Napoleon's victories the French went much grander and built the Arc de Triomphe in Paris, which is now even more cut off by traffic than Marble Arch," explained Grandad.

"Gosh," said the girl, "when Marble Arch was in front of the Palace you wouldn't be able to see the balcony and then we wouldn't be able to see the Queen."

"Good point," said Grandad, "the balcony has become the place where the Royal Family and the rest of us meet."

"However," he continued, "it wasn't until Queen Victoria came to the throne in 1837 that the Royal Family moved into Buckingham Palace."

15

"Did Victoria like it?" asked the boy.

"Not at first," replied Grandad.

"Why not?" asked the boy.

"I have found this interesting cartoon from 1843. Victoria and Albert are shown to be claiming that they are in *Real Distress* and that they haven't known *the blessing of a comfortable residence*," said Grandad, sharing the image.

"Really?" asked the girl." But how can you be in distress when you live in a palace?"

"That's rather heavy irony from the cartoonist. Of course, when you are asking for £150,000 to improve your home, which would be at least £19 million today, you are not poor. But Victoria and Albert complained that the royal apartments were above workshops and so they were bothered by noise and the smell of glue and oil."

"I like the boy with the hoop who is grinning at them," laughed the boy. "He doesn't mind the smell of glue."

A CASE OF REAL DISTRESS

"GOOD PEOPLE, PRAY TAKE COMPASSION UPON US. IT IS NOW NEARLY SEVEN YEARS SINCE WE HAVE EITHER OF US KNOWN THE BLESSING OF A COMFORTABLE RESIDENCE. IF YOU DO NOT BELIEVE US, GOOD PEOPLE, COME AND SEE WHERE WE LIVE, AT BUCKINGHAM PALACE, AND YOU WILL BE SATISFIED THAT THERE IS NO DECEPTION IN OUR STORY. SUCH IS OUR DISTRESS, THAT WE SHOULD BE TRULY GRATEFUL FOR THE BLESSING OF A COMFORTABLE TWO-PAIR BACK, WITH COMMONLY DECENT SLEEPING-ROOMS FOR OUR CHILDREN AND DOMESTICS. WITH OUR SLENDER MEANS, AND AN INCREASING FAMILY, WE DECLARE TO YOU THAT WE DO NOT KNOW WHAT TO DO. THE SUM OF ONE HUNDRED AND FIFTY THOUSAND POUNDS WILL BE ALL THAT WILL BE REQUIRED TO MAKE THE NEEDFUL ALTERATIONS IN OUR DWELLING. DO, GOOD PEOPLE, BESTOW YOUR CHARITY TO THIS LITTLE AMOUNT, AND MAY YOU NEVER LIVE TO FEEL THE WANT OR SO SMALL A TRIFLE."

"Where did they get the money from?" asked the girl.

"The government of the day provided most of the money as the Palace was a matter of national prestige, but Victoria did sell the Royal Pavilion at Brighton. The main change was that the courtyard was enclosed by a new wing which became the front of the palace. When finished it looked like this," said Grandad showing another picture.

"It's not exactly like BucKINGham Palace now," said the boy with emphasis on the KING.

"No, the façade of Portland stone which we see now was not installed until 1913 at the request of George V. Here it is on the right."

"Yes, that's much better," said the girl, "that's what I expect BucQUEENham Palace to look like."

"How big is it?" asked the boy.

"You can see the extent of the Palace best when you look at aerial photographs," said Grandad. "The one on the left was taken in 1905 from a hot air balloon. This is the old Palace with the facade that Victoria and Albert had built. See there is no Victoria monument in front. That came later in 1911. The one on right is the Palace as we know it."

"How do we know if the Queen is in residence?" asked the girl.

"I know that," said the boy, "when she's in, her flag is flying."

"That's right," said Grandad, "the Royal Standard."

18

"I still can't get my head around how big it is," said the boy.

"How about if I told you that the guide-book says there are 775 rooms of which 19 are State Rooms for important events like giving dinner for American presidents."

"How many American presidents have had dinner at the Palace?" asked the girl.

"That I don't know exactly, but your uncle tells me that during Victoria's reign there were 18 American presidents, three of whom were assassinated. I don't think many of those 18 came to Buckingham Palace. Presidents didn't travel then as much as now. However, during Queen Elizabeth's reign there have been 14 presidents so far and I expect some of them visited. Certainly President Kennedy came because there are photos of him with the Queen at the Palace."

"What about the number of bedrooms?" asked the boy wanting to get more facts about the Palace.

"The guidebook says that there are 52 principal bedrooms and 188 staff bedrooms, but only 78 bathrooms!"

"So if every principal bedroom has a bathroom then that only leaves 26 bathrooms for 188 staff. There must be a long queue in the morning," laughed the boy.

"That's sounds like the BucQUEENham Palace idea where you play with something and imagine how absurd it could become," said Grandad with a smile.

"But BucQUEENham Palace isn't absurd," said the girl indignantly, "BucQUEENham Palace is here to stay."

19

"Well," said Grandad, "the Palace is certainly here to stay and to round off the zoom call here is the view from the garden looking at the back of it. If you ever get invited to a garden party by the Queen this is what you see. Must go, bye for now."

"Bye, Grandad, thanks so much, hope to see you soon," they called.

Acknowledgements

Tim Pearce (editing and philatelic advice), Miyoko Gamble, Grant and Maree Walker, Isabel Pearce (script), Satski Gamble, Richard and Victoria Baxter, David Lewthwaite, Jim McEwen, Andrew Gamble, Curtis Kendall, Hunter Gamble, Richard Reddaway, Nigel Soper, Keith Wade, Jane Wicks.

Illustrations

Cover Illustration copyright Roger FitzGerald, photography by Russell Harper

FACING PAGE 1 Buckingham Palace circa 1840 – *property of the author*

PAGE 1 Silhouettes – *Eladora/Shutterstock*, Buckingham Palace – *Ewelina W/ Shutterstock*

PAGE 2 Stamps Edward VII – *Ivan Vdovin/Alamy*,
George V – *Hipix/Alamy*,
Edward VIII – *Studioshots/Alamy*,
GeorgeVI – *Michael Seleznev/Alamy Stock Photo*

PAGE 3 Stamps Queen Victoria Penny reds – *property of a collector*,
Queen Victoria – Nova Scotia and Canada – *property of the author*

PAGE 4 Stamps Queen Elizabeth II – *PA Images/Alamy*,
Queen Elizabeth II Australia – *Chris Dorney/Alamy Stock Photo*

PAGE 5 Silhouette – *Eladora/Shutterstock*

PAGE 6 Line of succession – *copyright Isabel Pearce*

PAGE 8 Queen Victoria and 3 generations – The Sketch, August 30 1899 – *property of the author*

PAGE 9 George VI after coronation on balcony – *Corbis Historical, Hilton Deutsch/Getty Images*

PAGE 10 Royal Family on the balcony – *newsphoto/Alamy Stock Photo*

PAGE 12 Buckingham House by J.Barton for the Beauties of England and Wales. Queen Charlotte John Downman 1782. Hodgkins collection – *prints property of the author.*

PAGE 13 Buckingham Palace from the park – *property of the author*

PAGE 14 Map of London, Geographia 1932 – *property of the author*

PAGE 15 Marble Arch – *QQ7/Shutterstock*

PAGE 16 Cartoon " A Case of Real Distress" – *property of the author*

PAGE 17 Buckingham Palace 1858 C.W.Sheeres. Illustrated London News – *property of the author*
Buckingham Palace – *Ewelina W/Shutterstock*

PAGE 18 Buckingham Palace 1905 By Perceval Spencer ,Illustrated London News May 27 1905 – *property of the author.*
Buckingham Palace aerial view – *Joel Virgo/ Shutterstock*

PAGE 19 Silhouette - *Eladora/Shutterstock*

PAGE 20 Print of the rear view of Buckingham Palace by Alex Hermann Haig 1901 – *property of the author*

PAGE 22 Children's silhouettes – *Eladora/Shutterstock*, 50p Piece – *kavalenkava/Shutterstock*

Questions for you

1. Who bought Buckingham House for his wife?

2. How many of Queen Charlotte's children became kings?

3. Which member of the Royal family knew Queen Victoria and Queen Elizabeth well?

4. Which of the four kings from 1901-1952 had the shortest reign?

5. How much did Buckingham Palace cost to rebuild for Queen Victoria?

6. Why did Victoria and Albert want to rebuild?

7. When did Queen Elizabeth II become Queen?

8. How old will you be in 2100?

9. Who designed the first Buckingham Palace for George IV?

10. How many rooms are there in Buckingham Palace?